Happy New Year Emily
"2002"

Love, Grandma

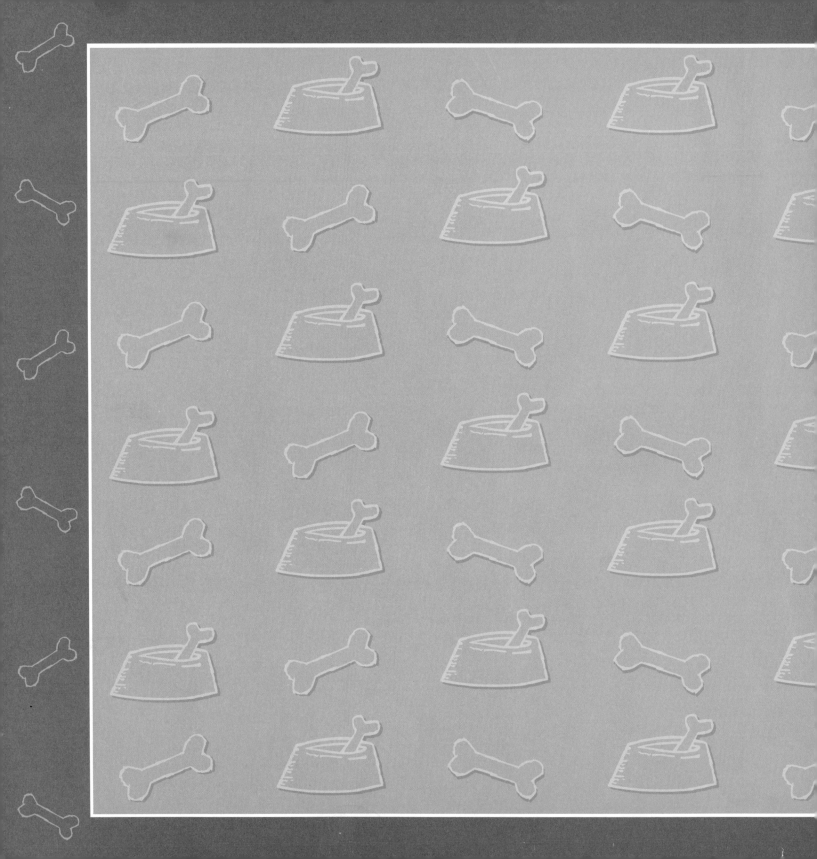

NORMAN BRIDWELL

Clifford®
Celebrates the Year

SCHOLASTIC INC.

New York   Toronto   London   Auckland   Sydney
Mexico City   New Delhi   Hong Kong   Buenos Aires

ISBN 0-439-35683-0

10 9 8 7 6 5 4 3 2 1   01 02 03 04 05
Printed in Singapore
First printing, November 2001

Table of Contents

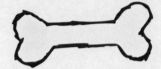

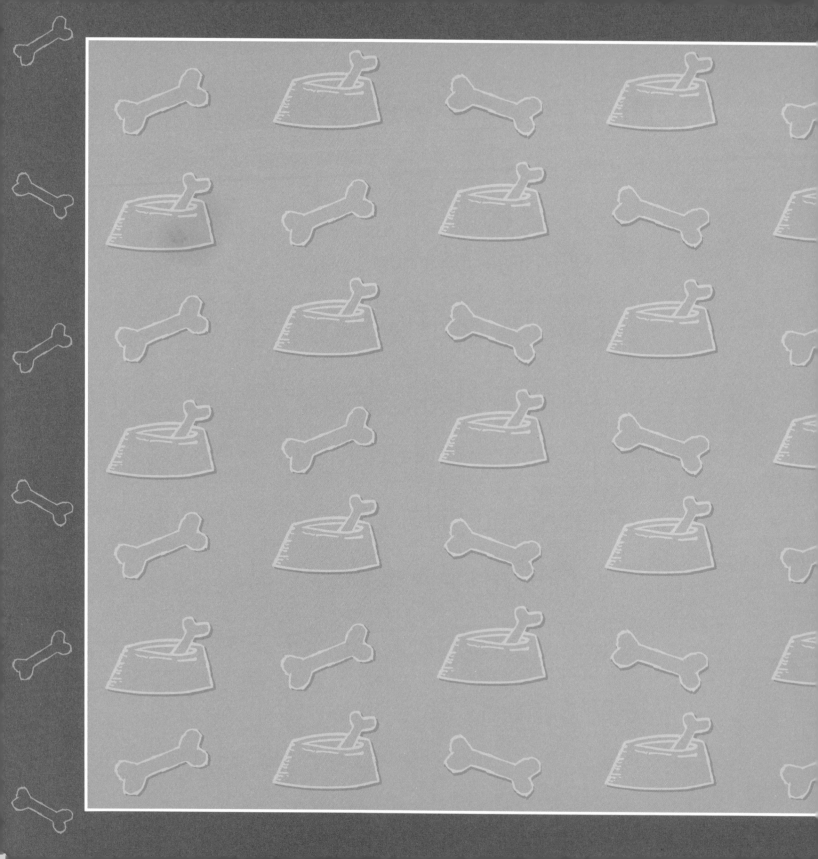

Clifford,®
WE LOVE YOU

IT'S CLIFFORD!

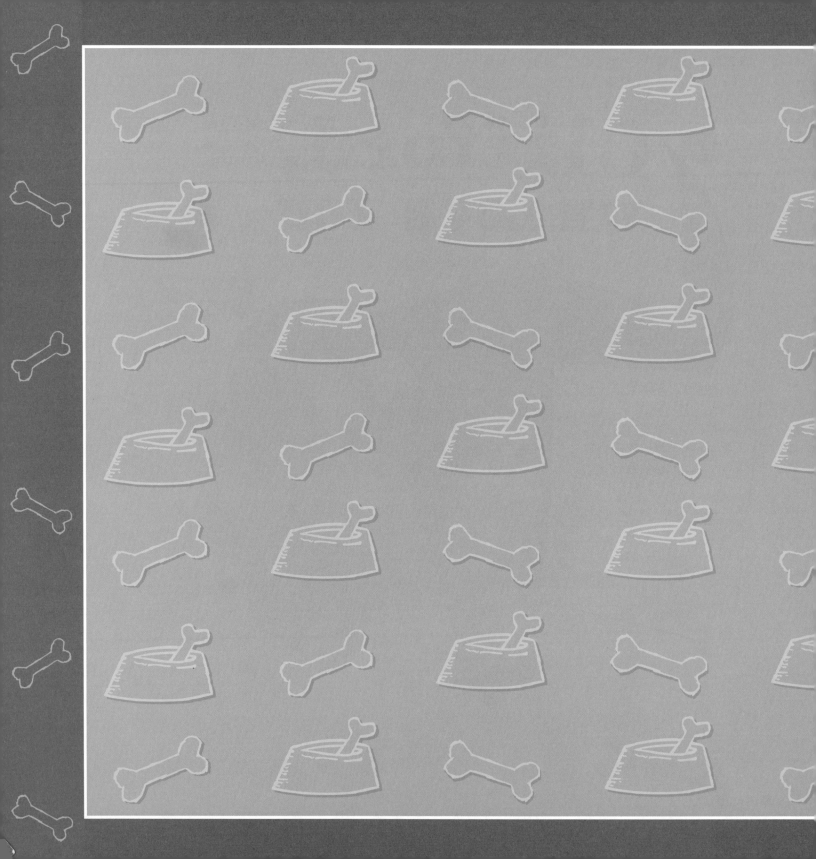

Clifford was feeling down-in-the-dumps.

I didn't know what to do.

I tried everything to cheer him up.

I served his favorite foods.
He wouldn't touch them.

My friend Alison thought some pretty flowers
might cheer Clifford up.

AH-CHOO!

They didn't.

Clifford loves parades. The kids in the neighborhood
put on a parade for him.

He felt worse than ever. Bill and Marcia said
they would cheer him up with a puppet show.

The show was very good.
He liked it, but then...

...when the witch tried to push the girl
and boy into the oven,

Clifford got upset.

I had an idea. I decided to write a
happy song for Clifford.

I thought of words that say all the wonderful things about Clifford. I put the words to a tune.

We sang my song to Clifford.
This is how it goes...

Who's the biggest dog around?
Who's the reddest dog in town?

Emily Elizabeth loved that pup...
Loved him so that he grew up.

It's Clifford! It's Clifford!
Lovable, laughable Clifford!
It's Clifford! It's Clifford!
Good old Clifford—yeah! The Big Red Dog!

Who can be a scary ghost?
Who do children love the most?

Who takes Emily for a ride?
Who is always by her side?

It's Clifford! It's Clifford!
Lovable, laughable Clifford!
It's Clifford! It's Clifford!
Good old Clifford—yeah! The Big Red Dog!

Who waits for Emily after school?

Who takes a bath in a swimming pool?

Who tries always to be good?
Who once starred in Hollywood?

It's Clifford! It's Clifford!
Lovable, laughable Clifford!
It's Clifford! It's Clifford!
Good old Clifford—yeah! The Big Red Dog!

Who is Emily's Valentine?
Who makes every day so fine?

Every day they have a ball.
He's the best (WOOF!) dog of all.

It's Clifford! It's Clifford!

Lovable, laughable Clifford!

It's Clifford! It's Clifford!

Good old Clifford—yeah! The Big Red Dog!

The song made Clifford feel much better.

Maybe you would like to sing it, too?

IT'S CLIFFORD!

words and music by Maureen Lee

1. Who's the big-gest dog a-round? *(handjive clapping)* Who's the red-dest
2. Who can be a sca-ry ghost? Who do chil-dren
3. Who waits for Em-i-ly af-ter school? Who takes a bath in a
4. Who is Em-i-ly's Val-en-tine? Who makes ev-'ry

dog in town? *(handjive clapping)* Em-i-ly E-liz-a-beth loved that pup,
love the most? Who takes Em-i-ly for a ride?
swim-ming pool? Who tries al-ways to be good?
day so fine? Ev-'ry day they have a ball!

(handjive clapping) Loved him so that he grew up. *(handjive clapping)*
Who is al-ways by her side?
Who once starred in Hol-ly wood?
He's the best (WOOF!) dog of all! It's

Clif-ford (It's Clif-ford!) Lov-a-ble, laugh-a-ble Clif-ford! It's Clif-ford! (It's

Clif-ford!) Good old Clif-ford-yeah! The Big Red Dog!
(Can be spoken.)

Clifford's® BIRTHDAY PARTY

My name is Emily Elizabeth,
and this is my dog Clifford.
Last week was Clifford's birthday.
We invited his pals to a party.

Mom had ice cream and cookies.

We put up decorations.

When it was time for the party to begin,
nobody was there.
Where could they be?

We went looking for Clifford's pals.

They were all together at the playground.

I asked them why they hadn't come to the party.

and everyone came to the party.

First we opened the gift from Scott and his dog Susie.
Scott had blown it up as much as he could.

Clifford blew it up some more.

We really had a ball.

Then Clifford pulled out the stopper.

That was a mistake.

The next gift was from Sam and his dog Lenny.
It was a piñata!

We hung the piñata from a tree.
There were treats inside for all the dogs.

Clifford was supposed to break the piñata
with a stick.
He gave a couple of good swings...

and the piñata broke open.
The dogs liked the treats...

but we decided not to give Clifford any more piñatas.

Alisha and Nero's gift was a toy dog that talked.

Clifford thought it was cute.

He went to pet it.

Uh-oh.

They don't make toys the way they used to.

It was time for ice cream when Cynthia
and her dog Basker arrived.

They brought Clifford a gift certificate
from the Bow Wow Beauty Parlor.
He could get a free shampoo and haircut.

We each had our own idea of how Clifford might look
after the beauty parlor.

I like Clifford just the way he is.
I thanked Cynthia for the gift,
but I slipped the certificate to Scott
and Susie. I knew she would like it.

Then came the cake. Clifford was surprised.

He was even more surprised...

when his family popped out!

He hadn't seen his mother and father
and sisters and brother for a long time.

Clifford liked the presents his friends gave him,
but having his family and friends with him
was the best birthday present of all.

Clifford's®
Happy Easter

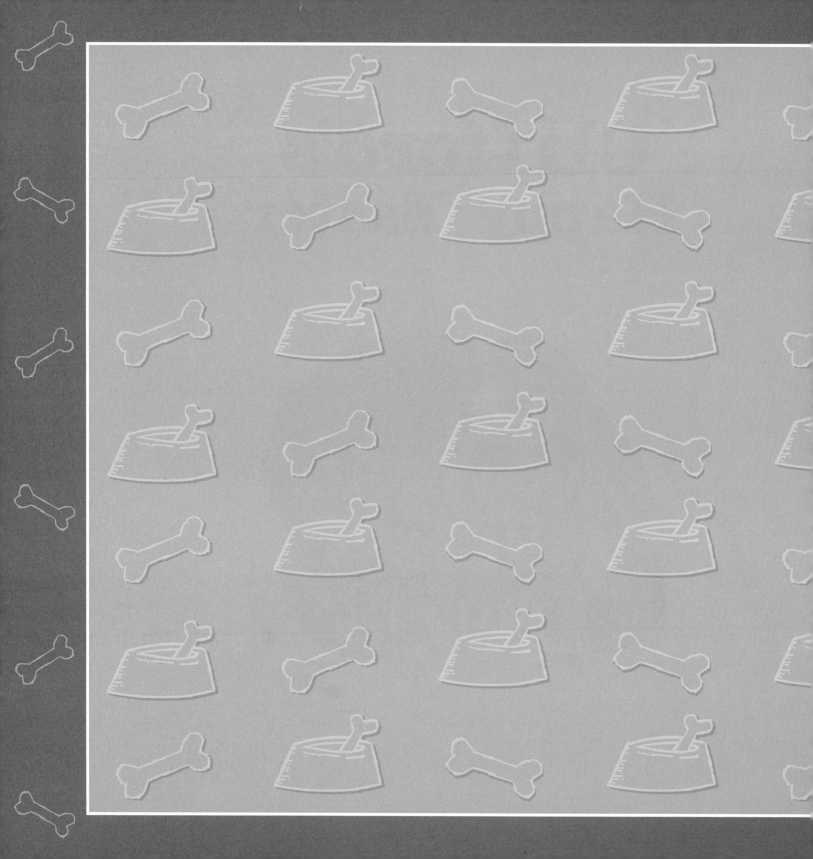

Hi! I'm Emily Elizabeth, and I love spring.
So does my dog Clifford.

The best part of springtime is Easter.

Last spring Mom and Dad brought us
a lot of eggs to color for the big Easter egg hunt.

On the day before Easter, I dyed the eggs.
Clifford wanted to help.
Poor Clifford. He wasn't very good at painting eggs.

So Clifford helped by watching me decorate the eggs.
He's a good watcher.

When I went to bed that night,
I fell asleep dreaming about Easter eggs.

It was a beautiful dream. Clifford was stirring
a giant tub of dye while I tossed in the eggs.

But then Clifford lost his balance!
He tumbled into the tub of dye.

Something surprising began to happen....

Suddenly Clifford was bright green!

It was just like St. Patrick's Day.

Then he turned sunshine-yellow!
This was becoming a very strange dream.

I grabbed a brush and began to dab on purple polka dots.
Clifford looked good in polka dots, but —

— they didn't last long.
The purple dots turned into squares,
and Clifford looked like . . .

...a giant checkerboard!

I didn't like that. I threw on some more dye.

I always used to wonder if I dreamed in color.

Now I know.

This was too much.

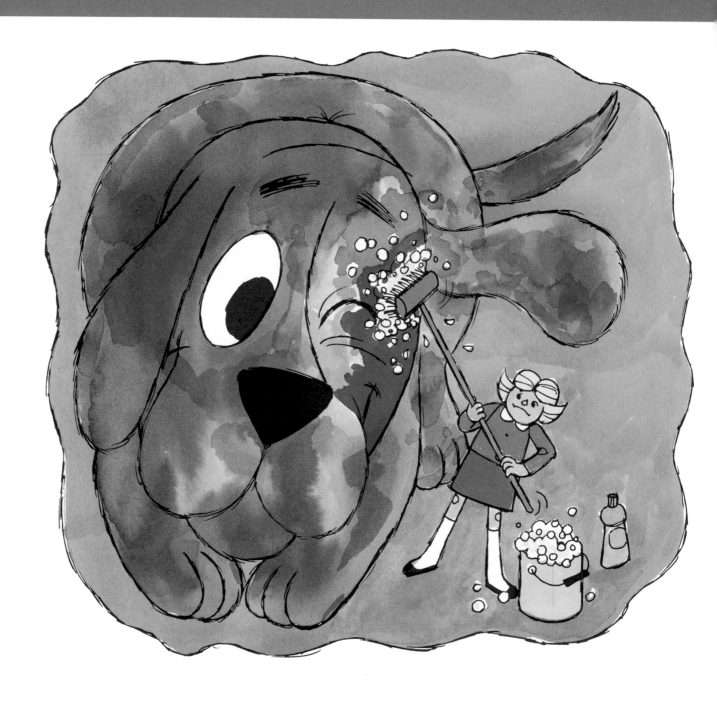

I tried to scrub the dye off Clifford. I was getting frantic...

...then I woke up.
It was Easter morning, and the sun was shining.

I ran out to see Clifford.
Thank goodness he looked just the same as always.
Good old Clifford.

We joined my friends and set off on the Easter egg hunt.

We looked high.

We looked low.

Clifford looked in places I would not have thought of.

Clifford's® SPRING CLEAN-UP

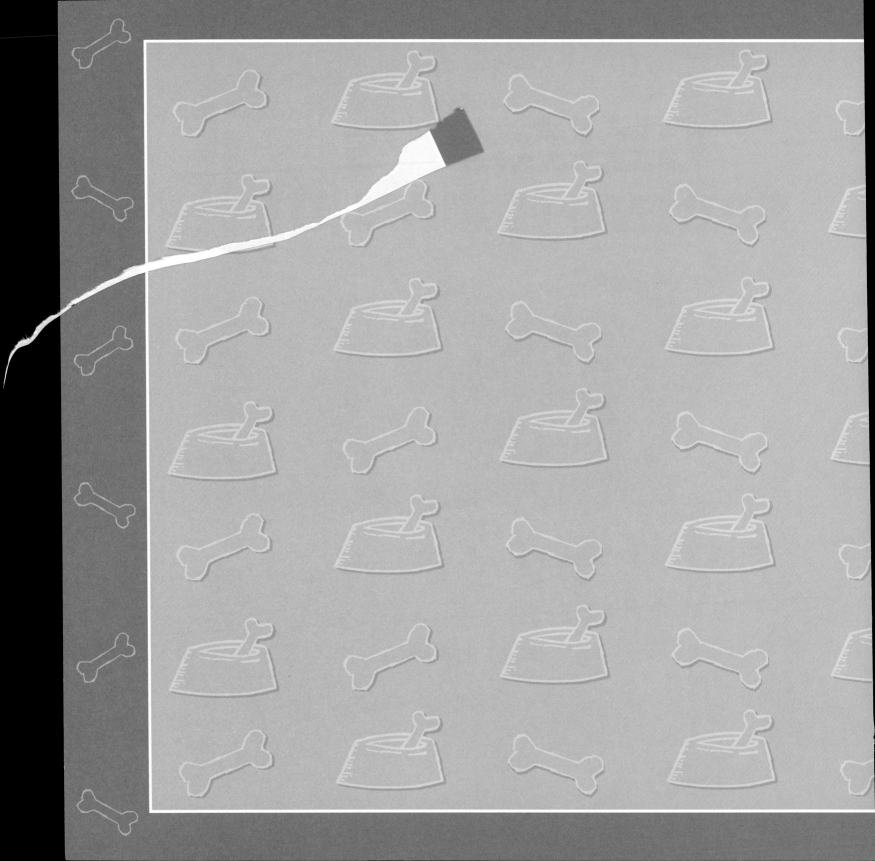

Happy spring! I'm Emily Elizabeth.

At our house, it's time for spring cleaning again.

Last year, the whole family worked hard—

even my big red dog, Clifford.

My first job was to hang some rugs out to air.

Clifford wanted to help.

He took a rug outside and gave it a good shaking.

I guess he shook it a little too hard.
Mom said we might as well wax the living room floor
as long as the rug was up.

Mommy and Daddy started to move the furniture outside.

When Clifford saw the couch, his eyes lit up.
He used to curl up on it when he was a small puppy.

CRUNCH!

He didn't fit on it anymore.

Good thing the couch was so old.

Daddy was going to get a new one anyway.

Poor Daddy. He had to rake the yard.
It looked as if it would take him all day.

But not with Clifford to help!

Just then some of my friends came by.

They asked me to help them clean up the vacant lot
on the corner. It was their Earth Day project.

Clifford did his part for Earth Day.

Then we planted a beautiful garden.

On the way home, Clifford and I saw some people
working on another Earth Day project.

Clifford gave them a hand . . .

er, a tail.

Back at home, there was another job to do.
Clifford's house needed some spring cleaning, too.

He swept out his old bones . . .

. . . and tossed out his collection of rubber toys.

It made quite a large pile.

Somehow Clifford got it all into
the garbage truck —

much to the surprise of the driver.

Now both our houses were neat and clean.
It was a good day's work.

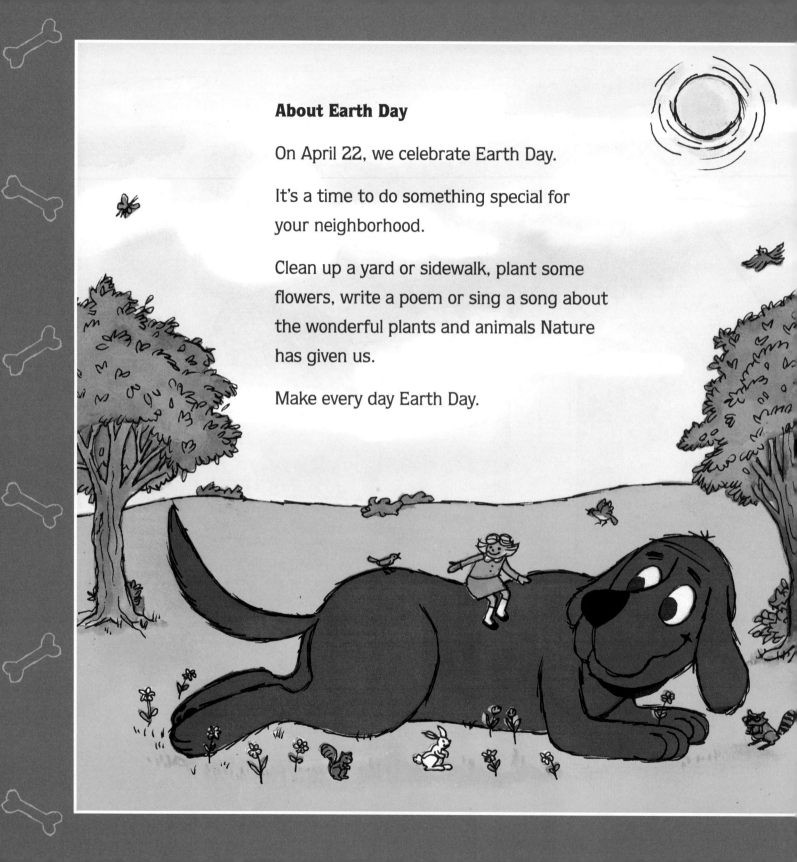

About Earth Day

On April 22, we celebrate Earth Day.

It's a time to do something special for your neighborhood.

Clean up a yard or sidewalk, plant some flowers, write a poem or sing a song about the wonderful plants and animals Nature has given us.

Make every day Earth Day.

Clifford®
and the BIG PARADE

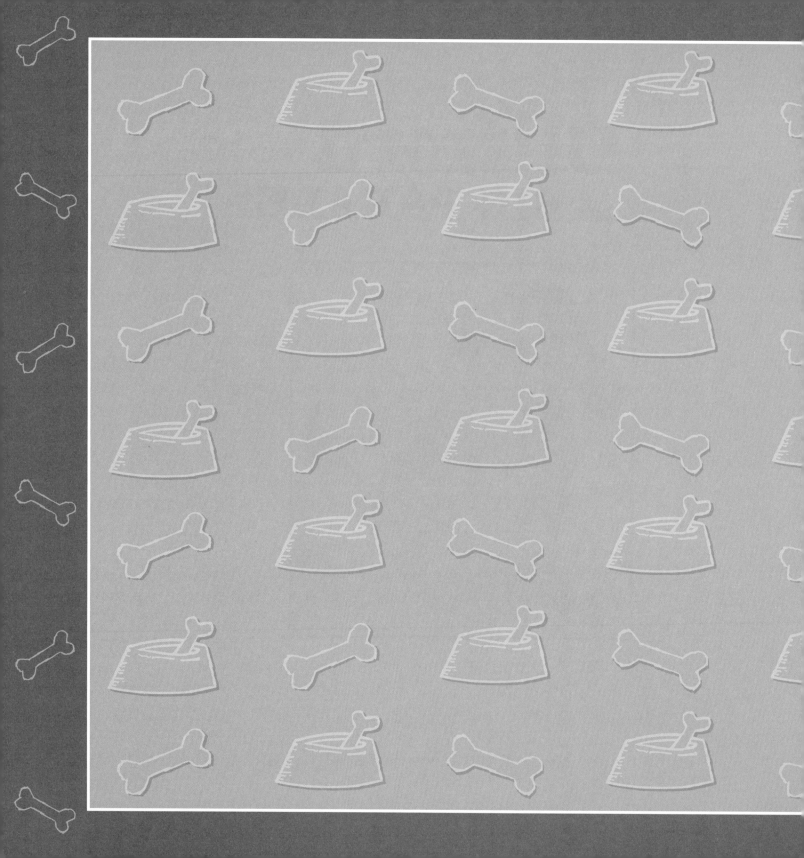

I'm Emily Elizabeth and Clifford is my dog.

We live in a great town.

Last year our town celebrated its birthday

with special events and a big parade.

Everyone wanted to look the way people did 100 years ago.

They dressed up in old-fashioned clothes, and

a lot of the men grew beards.

Clifford and I dressed up, too.
Clifford looked good in the fake beard I made for him.

We went to the city park
to see the old-fashioned games
and contests.

One team of old horses in the log-pulling contest was
having a hard time.
Clifford felt sorry for them.

He gave them some help.

Clifford wanted to join the bicycle obstacle race.
He couldn't ride a bike, so...

...he got in the race as an obstacle. He was a good one.

Some men were pitching horseshoes.
Clifford wanted to try that, too.

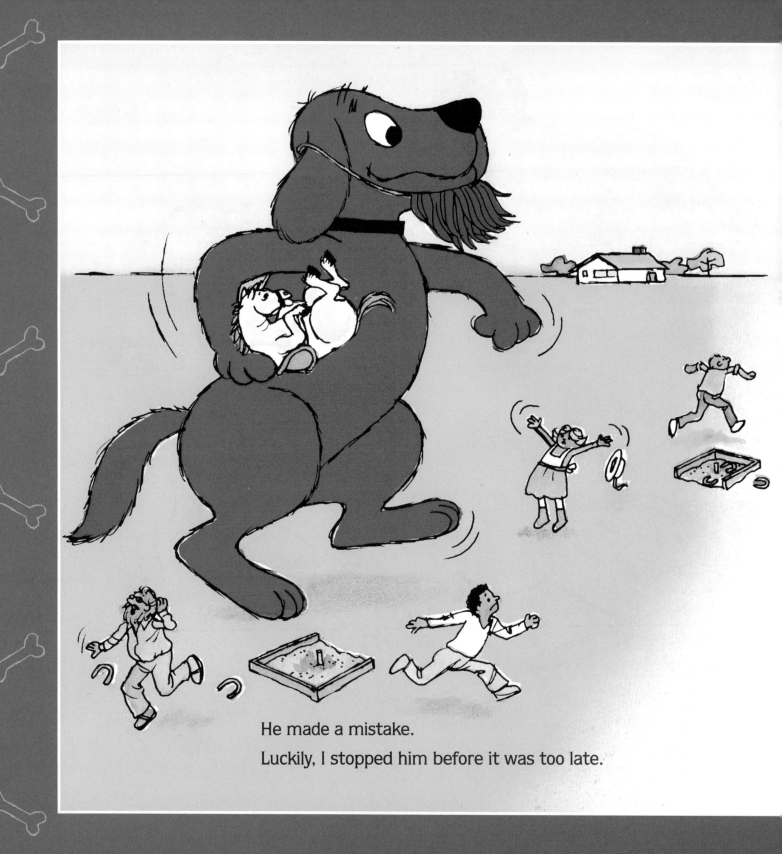

He made a mistake.

Luckily, I stopped him before it was too late.

Next, we played volleyball.

Clifford was keeping his eye on the ball…

... but he forgot about the net.

Poor Clifford. Volleyball was not his game.

We saw some people getting ready for a pie-eating contest.
Now that looked like something Clifford would enjoy.

It was. Clifford was the champion pie eater.

With a big red dog like Clifford,
every day is fun. But holidays are
the most fun of all.

At Christmas, Clifford makes a very good Santa.
He already has a red coat.

And on New Year's Eve, we stay up until midnight
so Clifford can blow his New Year's horn —

Happy New Year.

On Valentine's day —

— Clifford is my favorite valentine.

And you should see Clifford on Easter.
He makes a wonderful Easter bunny.

On April Fool's Day,
Clifford never plays tricks on anyone . . .

and no one plays tricks on Clifford.

On Thanksgiving, Clifford gets a great big turkey.

But today is the best holiday of all —

HALLOWEEN!

Last year we had a big Halloween party.
I dressed as a pirate, but I didn't know
how to dress Clifford.

Daddy thought Clifford would make a good devil.

I wanted him
to be a clown . . .

or maybe a witch.

But Clifford wanted to be —

a ghost.

When the children came to the party,
nobody could guess who the big ghost
really was.

We had fun.
We bobbed for apples.

Clifford wanted to play, too.

Then Mommy told us a ghost story.
But we weren't afraid . . . .

We had the biggest ghost on our street
taking care of us.

After the party, Clifford and I
went trick-or-treating.

We didn't have much luck.
But we didn't mind.

It was time to go to bed anyhow.
Halloween was over.

And now Halloween has come again.
I am not going to be a pirate this year.
I am going to be a fairy princess.

But what should Clifford be?

An Indian?

A knight?

What do you suggest?

Clifford's®
THANKSGIVING VISIT

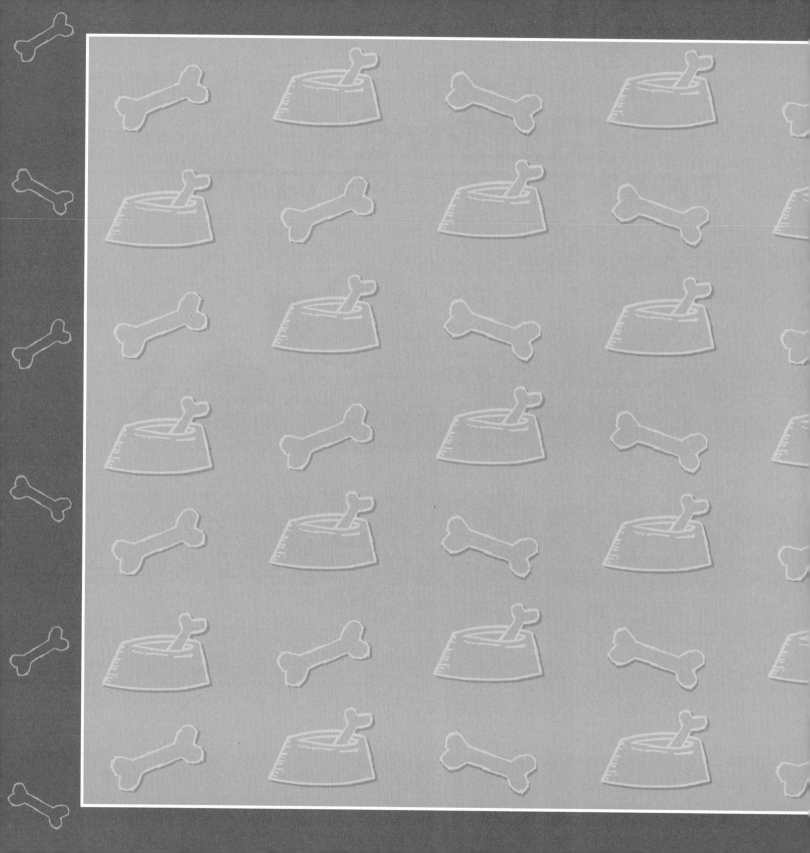

Hi! My name is Emily Elizabeth.

My dog Clifford and I have a lot of fun on Halloween.

Then, as soon as Halloween is over, we

start looking forward to Thanksgiving.

Last Thanksgiving my family flew away to visit my grandma. Clifford had to stay home. Our neighbors took care of him.

They were very kind, but Clifford got lonely.
He thought about his own family—
his father, his sisters, Bonnie and Claudia,
his brother, Nero. They all live in different places.

Most of all Clifford thought about his mom.
He decided to spend Thanksgiving with her.
She lives in the city.

Early Thanksgiving morning, Clifford started out.
It was easy. There weren't many cars.

But as he got near the city, there were a *lot* of cars.
Everybody seemed to be going to see their moms.

Some drivers were in a hurry.
They bumped into Clifford and honked at him.

Clifford came to a bridge. There were no cars on it.
They had all stopped. Clifford wondered why.

Soon he found out. It was a drawbridge!
And it was opening right under Clifford!

Poor Clifford.

Clifford was wet and cold.

He didn't want to get back on the highway.

There was only one other way to go.

The tunnel was dark and narrow. Suddenly there was
a roar and a bright light in Clifford's eyes.

The train stopped. The people inside were
as surprised as Clifford was.

He couldn't turn around, so he pushed
the train back to the station.

Then he jumped up to the street.

He was in a strange neighborhood.
Nothing looked familiar.
Where was his mom?

Clifford saw a very tall building.
He climbed up to look around.

He could see his old neighborhood!
He could see his mom's home!
He jumped down and started walking.

He was almost there.
He passed some kids playing football in the park.

Clifford didn't mean to,
but he wound up in the game.

At last, he found his mom.

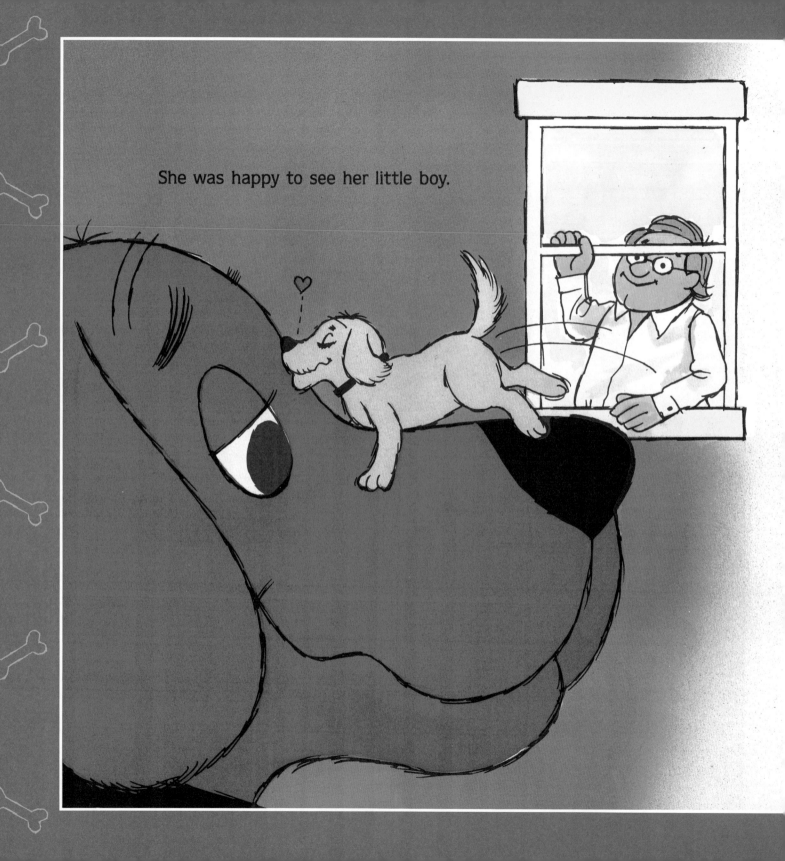

She was happy to see her little boy.

Her owner was happy, too.
He served them a nice Thanksgiving dinner.

I was having fun at grandma's house,
but I kept thinking about Clifford.
I wondered if he was thinking of me.

He was. He loves his mom, but as soon as
he could, he hurried home. So did I . . .

. . . because I am thankful for Clifford,
and he is thankful for me.

Clifford's® CHRISTMAS

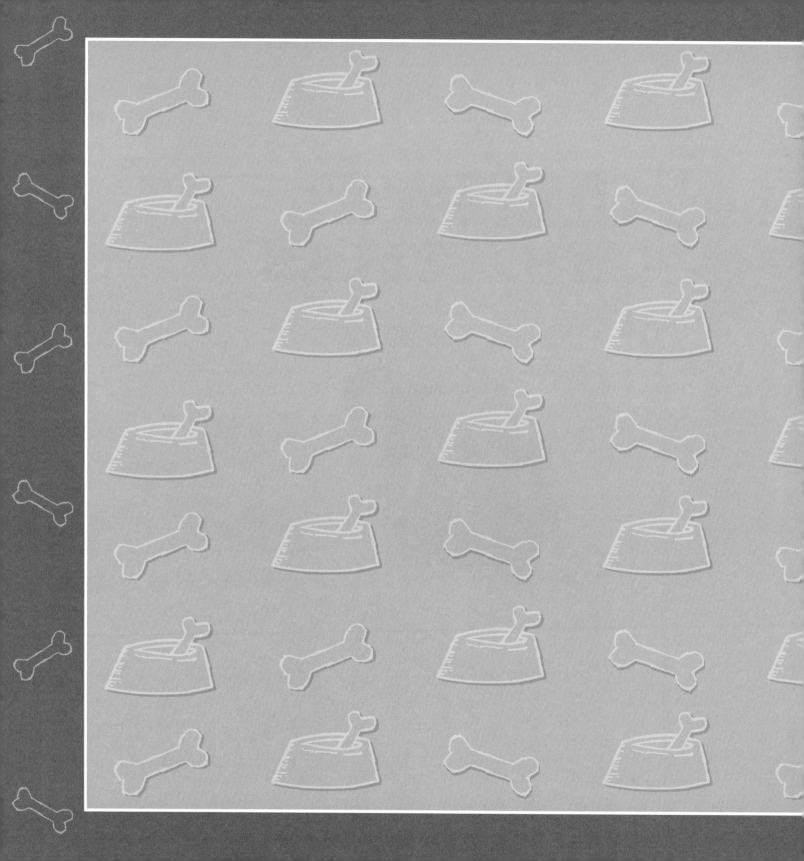

Hi! I'm Emily Elizabeth.

This is my dog Clifford.

Guess what holiday it is!

We start celebrating Christmas on Thanksgiving.
Last year we went to the Thanksgiving Day parade.
Clifford loved the big balloons.

At the end of the parade, Santa Claus came to town.

The Christmas season had begun!

Soon it started to snow.

My friends and I made a snowman.

Clifford made one too.

Later we went to the pond to play ice hockey.

We were having a great time until...

We decided that Clifford shouldn't play
ice hockey any more.

Christmas was getting closer and closer.

We counted the days.

One day Clifford saw some men digging up a tree.

He thought it would be a nice Christmas tree for us.

The tree was too big for our house...

but it was just right for Clifford's.

When Clifford was taking a nap,
my friends and I sneaked up on him
with some mistletoe.

Surprise!

At last it was Christmas Eve.

Clifford and I hung up his stocking.

I put some presents under Clifford's tree.

That night when we were sleeping
Santa came.

He landed on Clifford's roof.
He walked around looking
for a chimney...

Clifford woke up.

He heard someone calling for help.

Clifford helped. What a surprise!

Oh no — the bag of toys!

It had fallen into Clifford's water bowl.

The toys were ruined.

Clifford felt terrible. He had to do something.
So he offered Santa his own Christmas presents
to give to the children.

Santa smiled and patted Clifford.

He told him not to worry.

Then with a wave of his magic mittens,

Santa made the toys new again.

After leaving some toys at my house,
Santa got back in his sleigh.
He said good-bye to Clifford, and away
he flew until next year.

On Christmas morning
Clifford and I opened our presents.
It was a wonderful day.

And Clifford is a wonderful dog.

He makes every day Christmas Day.

Norman Bridwell's career got off to a big start with the publication of CLIFFORD THE BIG RED DOG. Thirty-eight years and many books later, Mr. Bridwell continues to enchant the picture-book crowd.

What makes Clifford so irresistible? Mr. Bridwell has his own theory: "I think Clifford's success is based on his not being perfect. Clifford always tries to do the right thing, but he does make mistakes."

Norman Bridwell, who was born and raised in Indiana, lives in Martha's Vineyard, Massachusetts.

Everyone Loves Clifford®!

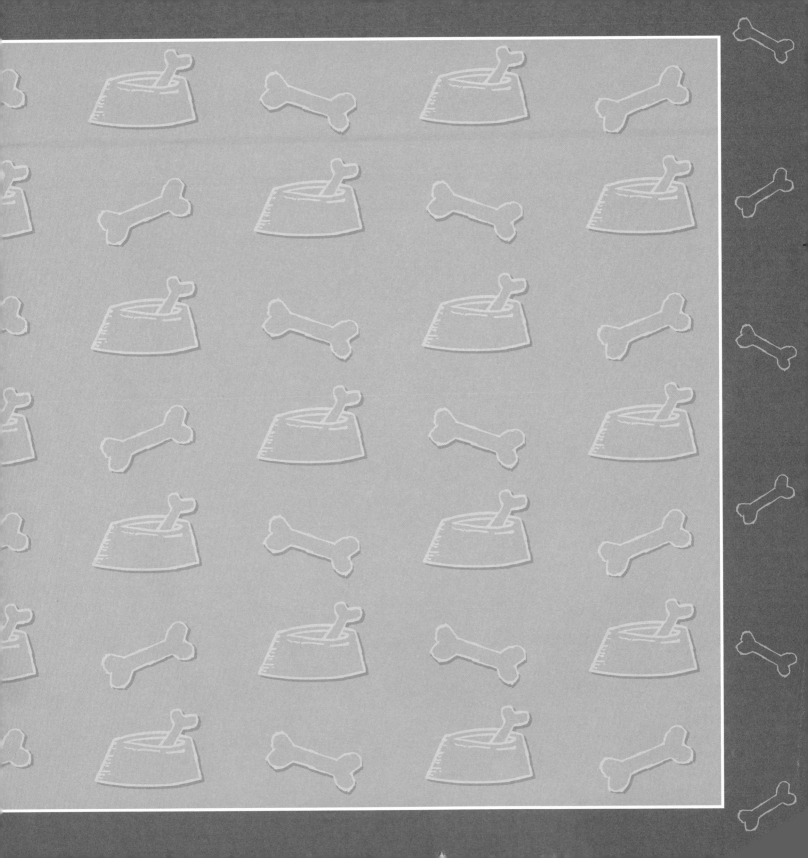

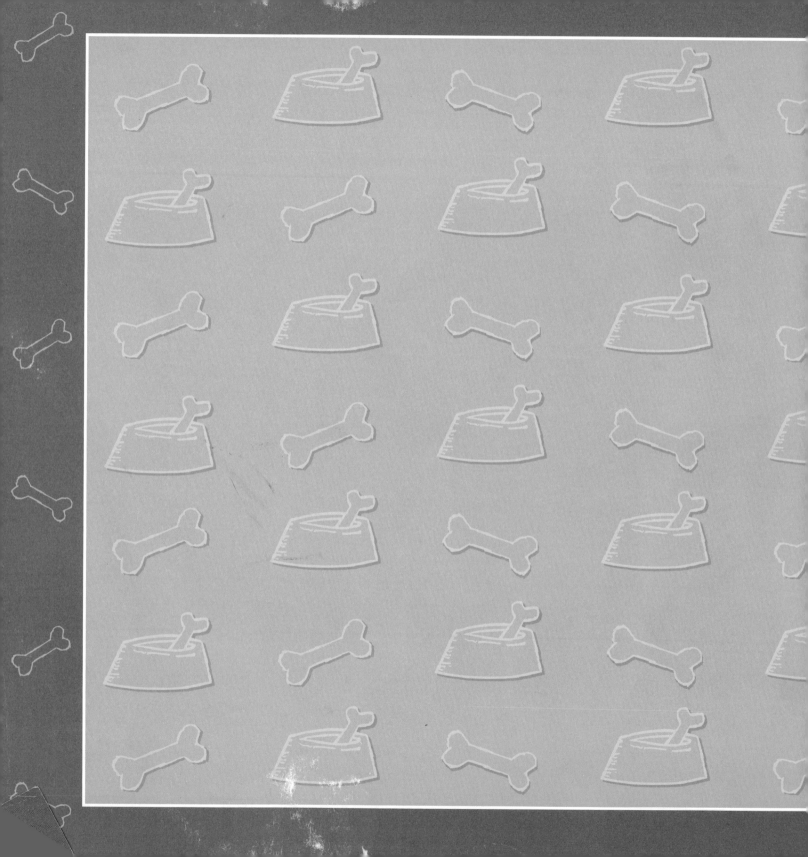